小气的托德

[美]达芙妮·斯金纳◎著
[美]约翰·耐兹◎绘
范晓星◎译

天津出版传媒集团

新蕾出版社

图书在版编目 (CIP) 数据

小气的托德/(美)达芙妮·斯金纳
(Daphne Skinner)著;(美)约翰·耐兹(John Nez)
绘;范晓星译.-- 天津:新蕾出版社,2016.9(2024.12 重印)
(数学帮帮忙·互动版)
书名原文:Tightwad Tod
ISBN 978-7-5307-6468-8

Ⅰ.①小… Ⅱ.①达…②约…③范… Ⅲ.①数学-
儿童读物Ⅳ.①O1-49

中国版本图书馆 CIP 数据核字(2016)第 201531 号

出版发行:天津出版传媒集团
新蕾出版社
http://www.newbuds.com.cn
地　　址:天津市和平区西康路 35 号(300051)
出 版 人:马玉秀
电　　话:总编办(022)23332422
发行部(022)23332679　23332351
传　　真:(022)23332422
经　　销:全国新华书店
印　　刷:天津新华印务有限公司
开　　本:787mm×1092mm　1/16
印　　张:3
版　　次:2016 年 9 月第 1 版　2024 年 12 月第 20 次印刷
定　　价:12.00 元

著作权所有,请勿擅用本书制作各类出版物,违者必究。
如发现印、装质量问题,影响阅读,请与本社发行部联系调换。
地址:天津市和平区西康路 35 号
电话:(022)23332351　邮编:300051

无处不在的数学

资深编辑　卢　江

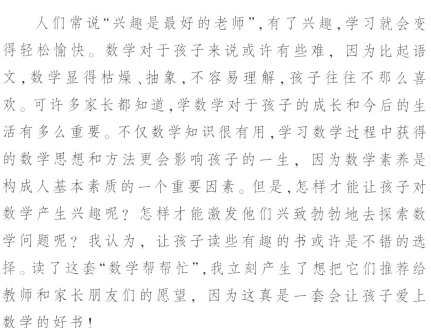

　　人们常说"兴趣是最好的老师"，有了兴趣，学习就会变得轻松愉快。数学对于孩子来说或许有些难，因为比起语文，数学显得枯燥、抽象，不容易理解，孩子往往不那么喜欢。可许多家长都知道，学数学对于孩子的成长和今后的生活有多么重要。不仅数学知识很有用，学习数学过程中获得的数学思想和方法更会影响孩子的一生，因为数学素养是构成人基本素质的一个重要因素。但是，怎样才能让孩子对数学产生兴趣呢？怎样才能激发他们兴致勃勃地去探索数学问题呢？我认为，让孩子读些有趣的书或许是不错的选择。读了这套"数学帮帮忙"，我立刻产生了想把它们推荐给教师和家长朋友们的愿望，因为这真是一套会让孩子爱上数学的好书！

　　这套有趣的图书从美国引进，原出版者是美国资深教育专家。每本书讲述一个孩子们生活中的故事，由故事中出现的问题自然地引入一个数学知识，然后通过运用数学知识解决问题。比如，从帮助外婆整理散落的纽扣引出分类，从为小狗记录藏骨头的地点引出空间方位等等。故事素材全部来源于孩子们的真实生活，不是童话，不是幻想，而是鲜活的生活实例。正是这些发生在孩子身边的故事，让孩子们懂得，数学无处不在并且非常有用；这些鲜活的实例也使得抽象的概念更易于理解，更容易激发孩子学习数学的兴趣，让他们逐渐爱上数学。这样的教育思想和方法与我国近年来提倡的数学教育理念是十分吻合的！

这是一套适合5~8岁孩子阅读的书，书中的有趣情节和生动的插画可以将抽象的数学问题直观化、形象化，为孩子的思维活动提供具体形象的支持。如果亲子共读的话，家长可以带领孩子推测情节的发展，探讨解决难题的办法，让孩子在愉悦的氛围中学到知识和方法。

值得教师和家长朋友们注意的是，在每本书的后面，出版者还加入了"互动课堂"及"互动练习"，一方面通过一些精心设计的活动让孩子巩固新学到的数学知识，进一步体会知识的含义和实际应用；另一方面帮助家长指导孩子阅读，体会故事中数学之外的道理，逐步提升孩子的阅读理解能力。

我相信孩子读过这套书后一定会明白，原来，数学不是烦恼，不是包袱，数学真能帮大忙！

托德是个小财迷。他喜欢得到零花钱和生日红包。有一次,他在路上捡到了一枚 1 角硬币,高兴了一整天。

　　托德从来不花自己的钱。他一收到钱就存好。他
有四个小猪存钱罐、一个装硬币的玻璃罐、一个钞票
夹和一个保险箱。这些东西里都装了钱。

　　在一个下雨的星期六,托德正在1角1角地数他的硬币。这时候,电话响了。

　　"托德!是杰克打来的!"托德的哥哥托比喊,"他要去看电影,你想跟他去吗?"

　　"不了,谢谢。"托德回答,"我正忙着呢。"

星期天，托德正在把一枚枚5角硬币用纸包起来。这时候，电话响了。

　　"托德！是杰克打来的！"托比喊，"他要去公园踢球，你想跟他去吗？"

　　"告诉他，我不去，谢谢了。"托德回答，"我正忙着呢。"

　　星期一，托德正在把一张张 1 元纸币用钞票夹夹起来。这时候，电话响了。

　　"托德！杰克要骑车去购物中心！你想跟他去吗？"托比问。

　　"不了，谢谢。"托德回答，"我正忙着呢。"

　　"托德，"托比说，"我开始担心你了，你除了数钱，其他什么事都不做。"

　　托德耸耸肩。他就是爱数钱。

　　托比从口袋里掏出一张 20 元的纸币。"你觉得你能把这钱花光吗？"他问。

　　"20 元？也许吧。"托德说。

"我打赌你花不光。"托比说,"你这家伙是个小气鬼。"

　　"我打赌我能花光。"托德说。他可不喜欢被叫作小气鬼。

　　"这是 20 元。"托比说,"如果你花不光的话,你不仅要把钱全额还给我,还要再加 5 元。成交？"

　　"成交。"托德说。

　　说完,他给杰克打电话去了。

去购物中心的路上，托德把自己跟哥哥打赌的事告诉了杰克。

"小菜一碟！"杰克说。他最喜欢花钱了。

他们来到宠物商店，杰克要买些鱼食。"你可以在这儿给你们家的小窝头买些什么。"杰克说。小窝头是托德的小狗。

托德有

"这根尼龙骨头怎么样？"杰克问。

"我不知道。"托德说。"3元太贵了。这又不是真正的骨头。"他把手里的20元纸币捏来捏去。

"可它们是真正的尼龙。"杰克说。

"哦，那好吧。"托德说。

¥ 3.00

托德付了

找回的钱是

接下来，他们来到书店。杰克看到一本《山地车世界》杂志，要 3.50 元。

"好贵。"托德说。

"可是这里有篇文章是关于在落基山骑车的。"杰克说，"我今年夏天要去那儿野营。我要买一本。"

托德有

托德看到一本杂志叫《钱币大观》，里面有介绍罕见的小猪存钱罐、古代钱币和最具收藏价值的钱币的文章。这本杂志要3元。托德看了一眼标价，把杂志放回了架子上。过了一会儿，他又拿了起来。

　　"托德！"杰克喊，"别磨蹭了！"

　　托德买下了杂志。

托德付了

找回的钱是

"我想吃点儿东西。"杰克说。

"我也是。"托德说。

他们在一家冰激凌店停下来。杰克看招牌上写了什么口味。托德只顾看价钱。

"嗯！巧克力香蕉甜筒。"杰克说。他买了一个。

托德有

14

"一个冰激凌要 2.30 元？"托德说，"太贵了。"

"是巧克力香蕉甜筒呀，不贵。"杰克说，"你尝一口。"

"哇！"托德说完也买了一个。

今日推荐
巧克力香蕉甜筒
￥2.30

2.30

托德付了

找回的钱是

两个人一边走，一边吃冰激凌，一直走到了鲍勃开的旧物店。

"鲍勃这儿有很多好东西。"杰克说，"看这本有落基山图片的年历。"

"那是去年的年历。"托德说，"不过我想里面的图片应该很漂亮。"

"所以我想买下来。"杰克说。

托德有

这时，他们看到了几个计算器。托德喜欢计算器。他看到一个太阳能计算器，还带音乐按钮。"无需电池！"他读道，"还能播放好几百首歌曲！"

"好酷！"杰克说，"咱们买了吧。"

托德买了那个计算器。

4.50

托德付了

找回的钱是

托德一边坐扶梯，一边试新买的计算器。它像铃铛一样发出叮叮当当的声音，帮托德算出来他还有7.20元要花。

"嘿！"杰克说。"欢乐帽子店打折呢！"

托德有

便帽
疯狂大特卖！

高尔夫球帽
清仓最低价！

雨伞帽
二五折！

杰克试了一下雨伞帽。

"我觉得不怎么样。"托德说。

19

托德看到一间照相亭。

"嗯，四张照片 3.20 元。"他说着拿出新买的计算器，"那也就是说每张照片只要 8 角。不错。"

托德有

　　托德自己照了两张照片。然后杰克挤进
照相亭,跟他合拍了两张。

¥ 3.20

托德付了

找回的钱是

去游戏厅的路上，他们在一家创意礼品商店门口停下。"哇，电子数币机。"托德说。

　　"正好适合你！"杰克说，"才 9.50 元。"

　　托德数了数自己的钱。"我不敢相信。"他说，"我只剩 4 元了。我真希望我的钱还够买这个……"

托德有

"托德！真高兴看见你！"说话的是艾达，托德的邻居，"我妈妈让我来买止咳糖，可是我的钱不够。"

"我就知道，我们刚才不应该买冰激凌吃。"艾达的朋友艾玛说。

"巧克力香蕉甜筒？"杰克问。

两个女孩点点头。"所以，你们能不能借我2元呢？"艾达问。

"当然。"托德说。

托德借给艾达

　　"我明天一定把钱还给你。"艾达保证说,"非常感谢你!"

　　"嘿!没问题。"托德说。

托德有　

"趁还没遇到别的朋友,我们还是先去游戏厅吧。"杰克说。

他们玩了一个游戏,又一个游戏……直到托德的钱全都花光了。

"真有趣。"托德说,"花钱如流水呀!我破产了。"他笑笑说:"看我告诉托比之后,他怎么说吧!"

每个游戏
¥ 0.20

托德付了

"哦，你把钱都花光了吗？"托德回到家时，托比问。

"是呀。"托德回答，"看看这些东西。我还借给艾达 2 元呢。"

"什么？你借钱给别人了？"托比问。

　　"是呀,她需要嘛。"托德说,"她会还我的。是不是这意味着我打赌输了?"

　　"没有!"托比说,"借钱给别人跟自己花钱一样好。"他跟托德击了击掌。"你赢了。"他说。

　　"所以,我不是小气鬼了?"托德说。

　　"还差得远呢。"托比说。

第二天，托德在放学的路上又去了一趟购物中心。

"那是什么？"托比见托德走上楼梯，问道。

"数币机。"托德说，"数得可快了。"

　　"等一下。"托比说,"你是说,你会花更
多时间数钱吗?"

　　"不。"托德回答,"我不会花那么多时
间数钱啦!我要花更多的时间享受生活。"

他做到了！

钱币表

艾达、杰克和托德去购物中心。

艾达买了：　　她付了：　　找回的钱：

¥ 7.00

我还有 3 元。

杰克买了：　　他付了：　　找回的钱：

¥ 3.50

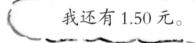
我还有 1.50 元。

托德买了：　　他付了：　　找回的钱：

¥ 2.30

我还有 0.70 元。

亲爱的家长朋友，请您和孩子一起完成下面这些内容，会有更大的收获哟！

提高阅读能力

● 请看书的封面，大声读出书名。请孩子说说画中的男孩在做什么，"小气"这个词是什么意思？

● 读过故事之后，请孩子想一想，托德的哥哥为什么叫他"小气鬼"？托德为什么决定去购物中心花些钱？

● 故事中的宠物商店有买一赠一的活动（参见第 11 页）。托德的狗一次只能啃一根骨头。问问孩子怎么买骨头最合算？

● 在第 27 页，托德的哥哥说："借钱给别人跟自己花钱一样好。"这句话是什么意思？为什么说借钱给别人跟自己把钱花掉一样好？借钱和花钱有什么不同？

巩固数学概念

• 请看第 32 页，准备好下列物品：一张 10 元纸币、一张 5 元纸币、三张 1 元纸币、一枚 5 角硬币和两枚 1 角硬币。可以用游戏钱币或请孩子用硬纸来做一些纸币和硬币代替。请孩子照着钱币表的三个情景表演一下。

• 托德付了 3.20 元在照相亭里拍照（参见第 20 页）。他用了数学里的什么运算，才知道每张照片多少钱？

• 托德回到创意礼品商店买数币机，花了 9.50 元。要是在托德回到购物中心之前，艾达就还给他 2 元的话，托德要从钞票夹里拿几张 1 元纸币，才能给售货员 10 元？售货员会找给他多少钱？

生活中的数学

• 用游戏钱币玩做买卖的游戏。在家中收集六件或者七件物品，请孩子给每件物品标价。家长假装成顾客，一件一件地买下所有物品。孩子做售货员，练习如何找钱。

• 当家长和孩子一起买东西的时候，偶尔鼓励孩子去付款。给孩子指出收银机上显示的物品价格，让孩子想想应该给收银员多少钱。请孩子看收银员如何找钱，并试着通过计算来确认找钱金额是否正确。

• 请孩子想想如果他要花光 20 元，他会买些什么，分别多少钱。然后，请孩子用减法减去相应的金额，直到 20 元花光为止。让孩子记住，要刚好花光 20 元，不能多也不能少。

托德拿着 100 元去玩具城买玩具。他买了两把水枪和一只泰迪熊，准备送给托比、杰克和艾达当新年礼物。水枪每把 20 元，泰迪熊每只 30 元，售货员应该找他多少钱？

¥10

¥20

¥30

艾达去逛超市,她发现自己最爱喝的饮料在进行"买二赠一"的促销活动。饮料每瓶3元,艾达花12元能买到几瓶饮料呢?

买二赠一

¥3.00

托比去百货公司买运动服,他挑中的运动服上衣 98 元,长裤比上衣便宜 20 元,短裤比长裤便宜 30 元,三件都买可以减 10 元,托比买一件上衣、一条长裤、一条短裤一共要花多少钱?

托德和托比一起去游乐园玩儿。托德买了一只熊猫气球、一桶爆米花和两根烤香肠后,他的20元零花钱还剩5元。熊猫气球每只5元,爆米花每桶4元,你知道烤香肠多少钱一根吗?

托德和杰克去市场买菜。他们买了两斤西红柿和一斤黄瓜,西红柿每斤 2.50 元,黄瓜每斤 3.20 元,他们一共要付给摊主多少钱?

杰克学校的小卖部在做购物满 30 元减 5 元的活动。杰克想买一些饼干,他喜欢吃的饼干每包 5.20 元,他买 6 包饼干能参加满减活动吗? 杰克实际支付金额是多少?

满 30 元减 5 元

　　艾达去商店买袜子，她选中的袜子每双2.30元，她要买4双。艾达手里拿着五张1元纸币、一张5元纸币、一张10元纸币和一枚5角硬币。艾达一共需要支付多少钱，她要怎样用手中的钱币进行支付呢?

互动练习 1：
30 元

互动练习 2：
6 瓶

互动练习 3：
214 元

互动练习 4：
每根 3 元

互动练习 5：
8.20 元

互动练习 6：
他能参加满减活动，实际支付
26.20 元。

互动练习 7：
一共要支付 9.20 元。有两种
支付方式：
方式一：支付四张 1 元纸币、
一张 5 元纸币和一枚 5 角硬
币，找零为三枚 1 角硬币。
方式二：支付一张 10 元纸币，
找零为一枚 5 角硬币和三枚
1 角硬币（或者为八枚 1 角硬
币）。

（习题设计：李卿怡）

Tightwad Tod

Tod liked money. He liked getting his allowance. He liked getting birthday checks. Once he found one jiao on the street and it made him happy all day long.

Tod never spent his money. Whenever he got some, he put it away. He had four piggy banks, a glass penny jar, a money clip, and a safe. They were all full.

One rainy Saturday Tod was counting his jiao coins when the phone rang.

"Tod! It's Jake!" called Tod's brother Toby. "He's going to the movies. Do you want to go with him?"

"No, thanks," answered Tod. "I'm busy."

On Sunday Tod was putting five-jiao coins into paper wrappers when the phone rang.

"Tod! It's Jake!" said Toby. "He's going to the park to play ball. Do you want to go?"

"Tell him no, thanks," answered Tod. "I'm busy."

On Monday Tod was folding one-yuan bills into his money clip when the phone rang.

"Tod! Jake's riding his bike to the mall. Do you want to go with him?" asked Toby.

"No, thanks," answered Tod. "I'm busy."

"Tod," Toby said, "I'm starting to worry about you. All you do is count your money."

Tod shrugged. He liked counting his money.

Toby pulled a twenty-yuan bill out of his pocket. "Do you think you could spend one of these? " he asked.

"A twenty? Maybe," said Tod.

"Bet you couldn't," said Toby. "You're too much of a tightwad."

"Bet I could," said Tod. He didn't like being called a tightwad.

"Then here's the twenty," said Toby. "But if you don't spend all of it, you have to give it back, plus five yuan. Deal? "

"Deal," said Tod.

And then he called Jake.

On the way to the mall, Tod told Jake about the bet.

"Piece of cake! " said Jake. He liked to spend money.

They went to the pet store so Jake could buy fish food. "You could get something for Waldo here," Jake said. Waldo was Tod's dog.

"How about this nylon bone? " asked Jake. "I don't know," said Tod. "Three yuan is a lot of money. And they're not even real bones." He turned the twenty-yuan bill over and over in his hands.

"They're real nylon," said Jake. "Well, okay," said Tod.

They went to the bookstore next. Jake found a copy of Mountain Bike magazine. It cost ¥3.50.

"That's expensive," said Tod.

"But it has a story about biking in the Rockies," said Jake. "I'm going camping there this summer. I've got to get it."

Tod saw a magazine called Coin World. It had stories about rare piggy banks, ancient coins, and the most valuable coin ever found. It cost ¥3.00. When Tod saw the price, he put the magazine back on the shelf. Then he picked it up again.

"Tod! " called Jake. "Come on! " Tod bought the magazine.

"I could use a snack," said Jake. "So could I," said Tod.

They stopped at the ice-cream store. Jake read the flavors. Tod read the prices.

"Mmmm! Chocolate Banana Gumbo," said Jake. He bought a cone. "¥2.30 for a cone?" said Tod. "That's expensive."

"Not for Chocolate Banana Gumbo," said Jake. "Taste this."

"Wow!" said Tod. He bought one, too.

They walked along eating their cones until they came to Bob's Bargains.

"Bob's has good stuff," said Jake. "Look at that Rocky Mountain calendar."

"It's last year's," said Tod. "I'll bet the pictures are nice, though."

"That's why I want it," said Jake.

Then they noticed the calculators. Tod liked calculators. He spotted a solar calculator with musical buttons. "No batteries required!" he read. "Plays hundreds of tunes!"

"Cool!" said Jake. "Let's buy it." Tod bought it.

Tod tried his new calculator on the up escalator. It made a chiming noise, like a tiny bell, and told him that he had ¥7.00 left to spend.

"Hey!" said Jake. "A sale at Happy Hats!"

Jake tried on an umbrella hat. "I don't think so," said Tod.

Tod spotted a photo booth.

"Hmm. Four pictures for ¥3.20," he said. He took out his new calculator. "That means each picture costs 8 jiao. Not bad."

Tod took two pictures by himself. Then Jake got in the booth with him, and they took two more.

On their way to the games arcade they stopped at The Gadgetorium. "Wow, an electronic money counter," said Tod.

"Perfect for you!" said Jake. "And it's only ¥9.50."

Tod counted his money. "I can't believe it," he said, "but I've only got ¥4 left. I wish I had enough money to buy..."

"Tod! Am I glad to see you!" It was Ada, his next-door neighbor. "My mom asked me to buy cough drops, but I don't have enough money."

"I knew we shouldn't have bought those ice cream cones," said Ada's friend, Emma.

"Chocolate Banana Gumbo? " asked Jake. The girls nodded. "So, can you lend me ¥2.00? " Ada asked. "Sure," Tod said.

"I'll pay you back tomorrow," Ada promised. "Thank you so much! "

"Hey! No problem," said Tod.

"Let's go to the arcade before we run into anybody else," said Jake.

They played one game and another and another... until all Tod's money was gone.

"That was fun," said Tod. "And it went so fast! I'm broke." He grinned. "Wait till I tell Toby! "

"Well, did you spend it all? " asked Toby, when Tod got home.

"Yes," said Tod. "Look at all this stuff. I even loaned Ada ¥2.00."

"What? You did? " said Toby.

"Well, she needed it," said Tod. "And she's paying me back. Does that mean I lose the bet? "

"Not at all," said Toby. "Lending is just as good as spending." He shook Tod's hand. "You win." he said.

"So I'm not a tightwad," said Tod. "Far from it," said Toby.

The next day Tod went to the mall again on his way home from school.

"What's that? " asked Toby, as Tod was heading upstairs.

"A money-counting machine," said Tod. "It works really fast."

"Wait a second," said Toby. "You mean you're going to spend even more time counting your money? "

"No," said Tod. "I'm going to spend less time counting my money—and a lot more time having fun."

And he did.